THE QUINLAN READERS

BASAL SERIES

To and Fro

A FIRST READER BY

MYRTLE BANKS QUINLAN

ILLUSTRATED BY CONSTANCE HEFFRON

AND KAYREN DRAPER

ALLYN AND BACON

BOSTON   NEW YORK   CHICAGO
ATLANTA   SAN FRANCISCO   DALLAS

COPYRIGHT, 1939

PRINTED IN THE UNITED STATES OF AMERICA

STORIES TO READ

Airplane Ride

Farm Friends

Farm Work

Farm Fun

Story Time

SOMETHING TO TELL

SONGS TO SING

Airplane Ride

Ready to Go

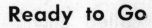

"Come, Jane," said Mother.
"Billy is in the car.
Baby is in the car, too.
Are you ready to go?"

"Yes, Mother," said Jane.
"I am ready to go now."

car

"Hurry, Jane, hurry!"
called Billy.
"Get into the car.
We must hurry to the airport."

"Oh, Mother!" said Jane.
"Let's hurry to the airport.
I want to go to the farm
in Father's airplane."

hurry   airport   airplane

At the Airport

"Here we are at the airport,"
said Billy.

"Where is Father?" asked Jane.

"There!" said Billy.
"There by the blue airplane."

"Hello, Father, hello!"
called the children.

hello

"Hello, there!" called Father.
"Are you ready to go?"

"Oh, yes, Father!" said Jane.
"It will be fun to go
with you in your airplane.
Grandmother and Grandfather
will be surprised."

"It will be fun for me, too,"
said Father.
"But we must hurry now.
It is time for us to go."

fun   Grandmother   Grandfather

4

Good-by

"Good-by!" said Mother.
"Be good to Grandmother.
Be good to Grandfather, too."

"Good-by, Mother!
Good-by, Baby!" said the children.

"Where is Winky?" asked Billy.

"I guess he is in the car,"
said Mother.

Going Up

" Whirr, whirr, whirr ! "
went the airplane.
" Whirr-rr-rr ! " it said.
Then up, up, up it went.

Billy waved at Mother and Baby.
Jane waved and waved, too.
" Good-by ! " she called.   " Good-by ! "

whirr   went

Up, up, up went the airplane!

"Look down, Jane!" said Billy.
"Look at the airport!
See how small it looks.
See how small the houses look.
See how small the trees look."

Up, up went the airplane!
Up it went, high into the air!

small   houses

Jane looked out of the window.
She called,
"Good-by, houses! Good-by, trees!
Good-by, airport!
We are going to the farm
to see Grandmother and Grandfather."

Billy looked and sang,
   "Big airplane, so very high,
     Will you fly up to the sky?"

The airplane said,
"Whirr, whirr, whirr!"

And it did go very high.
It did go up into the sky.
Father laughed at the children.

out

Tell —

Who was in the car.

Who wanted to hurry.

Who went to the airport.

Who said, "Hello, there!"

Who was by the airplane.

Who was having fun.

Who said, "Where is Winky?"

Who saw small houses.

Who looked out of the window.

Who went to see Grandmother.

Who went to see Grandfather.

Who laughed at the children.

Where Was Winky?

"Where was Winky?" asked Billy.

"Winky was not happy," said Jane.
"He wanted to go with us.
He wanted to see Grandmother
and Grandfather."

"Winky will be all right,"
said Father.
"He will have fun with Baby."

Just then they heard a little sound.

Billy looked at Jane.

Jane looked at Billy.

"What is it?" Jane asked.

"I do not know," said Billy.
"But I heard something."

"So did I," said Jane.

Just then they heard,
"Billy, Billy, let me out!
Let me out, Jane!
Please, please let me out!"

just   heard

Father laughed and said,
"Look in that box.
I think you will find a surprise."

Billy opened the box.
He looked in.   There sat Winky!

"Oh, Winky!" said Billy.
"What are you doing in that box?"

Jane said, "Come out, Winky!
What are you doing in that box?"

Winky climbed out.
He looked at Billy.

"I was not happy," he said.
"You were going to the farm.
I wanted to go, too.
I wanted to see Grandmother
and Grandfather.
Please let me go with you."

"Father," asked Billy,
"may Winky go?
He wants to see Grandmother
and Grandfather, too."

Father looked at Winky.
"Will you be a good monkey?"
he asked.

"Yes, yes!" said Winky.
"I will be very good.
I will be very, very good!"

"All right," said Father.
"You may go to the farm, too."

Do You Know —

Who was not happy?

Who heard a little sound?

Who said, "I heard something"?

Who said, "Let me out"?

Who opened the box?

Who was in the box?

Who looked at Winky?

Who wanted to see Grandmother?

Who wanted to see Grandfather?

Who said, "Come out, Winky"?

Who said, "I will be very good"?

Who said, "All right"?

Up in the Sky

"Whirr, whirr, whirr!"
said the airplane.

It went high, high, high.
It went high into the sky.

"Oh, what fun, what fun!"
cried Winky.
"I like to ride in this airplane."

"You will like the farm, too,"
said Billy.
"We shall have fun at the farm."

ride

"Shall we see some animals?"
asked Winky.

"We shall see many animals,"
said Billy

"Are farm animals our friends?"
asked Winky.

"Yes," said Jane.
"Farm animals are good friends."

"What fun!" said Winky.
"What animals shall we see?"

animals

"We shall see Bossy, the cow,"
said Jane.
"Bossy will give us some milk."

"Good, good!" said Winky.
"I shall like Bossy, the cow."

"We shall see Nicky, the horse,"
said Billy.
"Nicky will give us a ride."

"Oh, what fun!" said Winky.
"I want to ride Nicky, the horse."

Bossy   give   Nicky

18

"We shall see Fido, the dog,"
said Jane.

"Will Fido bark at me?"
asked Winky.

"No, no!" laughed Billy.
"Fido will not bark at you.
He will play with you."

"Will Fido give us a ride?"
asked Winky.

Father laughed.
"You will find out," he said.

Fido   bark

"And we shall see Polly," said Jane.

"Is Polly a girl?" asked Winky.

"Oh, no!" said Jane.
"Polly is a parrot."

"A parrot?" asked Winky.
"Will the parrot give us a ride?"

"No, no, Winky!" said Billy.
"A parrot is a bird."

"Will Polly bark at me?" asked Winky.

Father began to laugh again.
Billy and Jane laughed, too.
"You will see," they all said.

Polly   parrot   began

Guess Who

I am a farm animal.

I am not Bossy, the cow.

I am not Fido, the dog.

I am not Polly, the parrot.

Children like to ride me.

Guess who I am. Draw me.

I am a farm animal.

I do not bark at you.

You do not ride me.

I give good fresh milk.

Guess who I am. Draw me.

Going Down

"Whirr, whirr!" said the airplane.
Then it began to go down.
Down, down, down it went.

"Look!" said Father. "Look down!
What do you see?"

"Oh!" said Billy.   "I see a house!
It is Grandfather's house!"

"Look, Winky, look!" cried Jane.
"There is Grandfather's house.
And there is Grandfather!"

"And there is Grandmother, too,"
said Billy.
"See!   They are waving to us!"

The children waved and waved.
Winky began to wave, too.

Down, down went the airplane.

It went down to the ground.

"Whirr, whirr, whirr!" it said.

It ran on the ground.

Then it stopped.

It stopped close to Grandmother.

ground   stopped

At Grandfather's

Jane ran to Grandfather.

Billy ran to Grandmother.

"Here we are!" they cried.

Grandmother said,

"We are so glad to see you!"

Just then Grandfather saw Winky.

"Who is this?" he asked.

"This is Winky," said Jane.

"Winky is our pet monkey.

He wanted to see you, too."

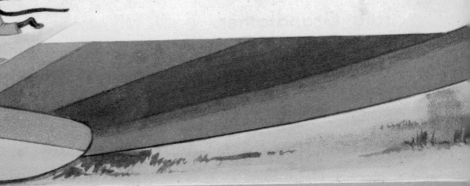

glad

Grandfather looked at Grandmother.
Grandmother looked at Grandfather.
They both looked at Winky.
Then they began to laugh.

"A pet monkey at our farm!"
said Grandfather.
"We are glad to see you."

"Oh, thank you," said Winky.
"I am glad to be here, too."

"Come, come," said Grandmother.

"Come into the house.

You must be hungry.

You shall have some fruit.

You shall have some milk, too."

Jane said, "We are hungry.

We like to eat fruit.

We like fresh milk, too."

Tell Who Said —

"What do you see?"

"They are waving to us."

"We are so glad to see you!"

"A pet monkey at our farm!"

"I am glad to be here, too."

"We stopped on the ground."

"Come into the house."

Something to Draw

Draw the airport.

Draw the blue airplane in the sky.

Draw Grandfather's house.

Whirr, Whirr, Whirr!

Words by
Myrtle B. Quinlan
Waltz tempo

Music by
Merle Montgomery

High in the sky Where the lit-tle birds fly, High in the sky so blue! Whirr, whirr, whirr, whirr! It's fun to fly high with you!

Farm Friends

The Next Morning

Jane and Billy were playing
with Fido the next morning.
Just then they heard,
"Pretty Polly! Pretty Polly!"

They looked up.
There sat Polly, the parrot.

"Hello, Polly!" said Billy and Jane.

"Hello, hello, hello!" said Polly.

Winky looked at Polly and laughed.
"What fun this is!" he said.

next   pretty

"Let's play a game with Polly,"
said Jane.
"Let's play 'Say What I Say.'"

"Yes, let's play 'Say What I Say,'"
said Billy.

Polly sat by her cage.
She looked at the children.
"Say what I say!" she said.
"Say what I say!"

her   cage

"Good morning, pretty Polly,"
said Jane.

"Good morning, Jane,'
said Polly.

Jane laughed.
"No, no, Polly!" she said.
"Just say what I say!"

"No, no, Polly!" said Polly.
"Just say what I say!"

Jane laughed and laughed.

"Watch me, Polly,"
said Winky. "Then do as I do."

Winky jumped over a table.
He jumped over a chair.

Polly sat by her cage.
She watched him.
But she did not jump.

"Watch me, Polly," said Billy.
"And do as I do."

Billy jumped up and down.
Polly watched him.
But she did not jump up and down.

as   him

Guess what Polly did then!
She went into her cage.
She jumped on her swing.
And she began to swing.

She said, "Watch me!
Do as I do.   Say what I say.
Hello, Polly! Pretty Polly!"

"All right," said Winky.
"I do not have a swing.
But I can swing by my tail."

How Jane and Billy laughed.
"Oh, what fun!" they said.

swing

Yes — No

Jane saw Polly the next morning.

Polly was a pretty parrot.

Billy sat by the cage.

Jane played games with Polly.

Winky jumped over a chair.

Polly watched the children.

Winky can swing by his tail.

The parrot went into her cage.

Jane began to swing high.

Polly jumped on her swing.

The parrot ate some oatmeal.

Grandmother stopped by the window.

Grandfather laughed at Polly.

Bunny Lee's Surprise

One morning Billy said,
"Grandmother, where is Bunny Lee?
May we see her?"

"Yes, Billy," said Grandmother.
"You may see her.
She has a fine surprise for you."

"A surprise!" said Billy.

"A surprise!" said Jane.

"What is it?" asked Billy.

"You will see," said Grandmother.

Bunny   has

Billy began to sing,

" Oh, Bunny Lee, Bunny Lee

Has a fine surprise for me."

Winky laughed and sang,

" Bunny Lee, hop to me.

Hop to me, my Bunny Lee."

hop

The children ran to Bunny Lee's house.

"Bunny Lee!" called Billy.
"What is your surprise?"

Bunny Lee said nothing.
But her funny little nose began
to wiggle, wiggle, wiggle.
Winky said, "Bunny Lee, hop to me."

Bunny Lee came hop, hop, hop.
She sat by Winky.
But she said nothing.

nothing   nose   wiggle

38

"I know," said Billy.

"Bunny Lee is hungry.

A rabbit likes to eat grass.

Let's get some grass for her."

"See this green grass," said Jane.

"It is for you, Bunny Lee."

Bunny Lee looked at the grass.

She said nothing.

But her funny little nose went

wiggle, wiggle, wiggle.

Then she ate the grass.

She ate and ate and ate the grass.

rabbit   grass

"Now, Bunny Lee," said Billy,
"what is your surprise?"

Bunny Lee said nothing.
But her funny little tail began
to wiggle, wiggle, wiggle.

Guess what she did then!
She hopped to her house.
And she looked in her door.
Then out hopped a baby rabbit.
It was a little white rabbit.

"Oh, pretty white rabbit!
Come to me," said Jane.
"I shall call you Pet."

door   white

Billy said, "Bunny Lee, Bunny Lee,
have you a fine surprise for me?"

Bunny Lee looked at Jane and Pet.
She hopped to her house again.
And she looked in her door.
Then out hopped a black rabbit.

Guess what the black rabbit did!
It hopped over to Billy.

"Oh, a black rabbit!" said Billy.
"I shall call you Night."

black   Night

Winky said, "Jane has a surprise.

She has Pet. Billy has a surprise.

He has Night.

I want a surprise, too."

So he said, "Bunny Lee,

have you a surprise for me?"

Bunny Lee looked at Jane and Pet.

She looked at Billy and Night.

Guess what she did then!

She hopped to her door.

And she went into her house.

"Oh, my!" cried Winky.
"Bunny Lee has no surprise for me."

Just then Bunny Lee hopped out
of her door.   Right behind her
was a little spotted rabbit.

"Oh — oh — oh!" cried Winky.
"Look, Billy!   Look, Jane!
A little spotted rabbit!
A pretty spotted rabbit just for me!"

behind   spotted

Do you know
what that little spotted rabbit did?
It hopped over to Winky.

Winky laughed and sang,
  "Bunny Lee, Bunny Lee
  And your little rabbits three,
  Thank you for the fine surprise,
  The fine surprise for me."

Tell the Right Words

1. Bunny Lee has —
   a cage, a car, a surprise.

2. Bunny Lee's nose began —
   to jump, to hurt, to wiggle.

3. Bunny Lee said —
   "nimble," nothing, "number."

4. Bunny Lee ate —
   the grass, the door, the night.

5. Bunny Lee has —
   three rabbits, two white eyes.

6. Spotted rabbit was —
   behind a car, behind Bunny Lee.

Looking for Specky

One day Billy said, "Come, Jane.
Let's find Specky, the hen."

Winky ran to Billy and Jane.
"May I go with you?" he asked.
"I want to see Specky, the hen.
I want to see her baby chicks.
I want to play with the chicks, too."

"Yes, Winky," said Billy.
"We are glad to have you with us."

Specky   hen   chicks

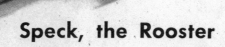

Speck, the Rooster

" Cock-a-doodle-doo !

Cock-a-doodle-doo ! "

said Speck, the rooster.

" Listen to me, listen to me !

Do not play with Specky, the hen.

Do not play with her baby chicks.

Cock-a-doodle-doo !

Cock-a-doodle-doo !

Listen to me, listen to me ! "

Billy said, " Oh, thank you, Speck !

We will listen to you."

rooster   cock-a-doodle-doo   listen

Specky, the Hen

Jane said,

" Good morning, Specky.

Where are your ten baby chicks ?

We want to see them."

" Cluck, cluck, cluck,"

said Specky, the hen.

" My chicks are under me.

Come, ten baby chicks !" she called.

" Jane wants to see you."

ten   cluck   under

Baby Chicks

"Cluck, cluck," said Specky again.
"Come, pretty little chicks!
Jane and Billy want to see you."

"I want to see them, too," said Winky.

Just then the children heard,
"Peep, peep, peep, peep!"

Then out came one yellow chick.

"Come out, come out!" called Jane.
"We want to see you."

Then out came two, three,
four little yellow chicks.

yellow   four

Billy said,

"The other chicks are under Specky.
We can not see them."

"Come, chick, chick, chick!"
called Jane.

Then out came all the other
little baby chicks.

Billy said, "Four yellow chicks,
four black chicks, two white chicks."

Specky said, "Cluck, cluck, cluck.
Here are my ten baby chicks."

"What pretty chicks!" said Jane.

other

Something to Tell

1. I am Specky, the hen.
   I said, "My chicks are under me."
   Tell something I can do.

2. I am Speck, the rooster.
   I said, "Listen to me, listen to me!"
   Tell something I can do.

3. We are ten baby chicks.
   We were under Mother Hen.
   Four of us are yellow.
   Four of us are black.
   Two of us are white.
   Tell something we can do.

Black Chick

The children watched the chicks
run and play.

Billy said, "Four yellow chicks,
two white chicks, four black chicks!"

Jane said, "No, no, Billy!
There are not four black chicks."

Billy looked at the chicks.
He counted one, two, three.
But he did not count four.
He looked again.
He did not see the other black chick.

counted

Billy said, "Look, Jane!
One black chick is not here!"

"Cluck, cluck, cluck!" said Specky.
"Come, chick, chick, chick!"

But the black chick did not come.

"Cluck, cluck!" said Specky again.
"Come, little Black Chick!
Come to your mother!"

But Black Chick did not come.

Just then they heard,
"Peep, peep! Mother, Mother!"

Specky listened.
Billy and Jane listened.

"Peep, peep!" they heard again.

Specky began to run.
Billy and Jane ran, too.
Then guess what they saw!
Winky? Yes, Winky!
And guess what he had!
He had little Black Chick!

had

Specky ran at Winky.

"Cluck, cluck, cluck!" she cried.

"Let my baby go! Let my baby go!"

Then she jumped at Winky.

"Oh, my! Oh, my!" said Winky.

"Here is your baby chick.

I just wanted to play with it."

Speck, the rooster, said,
" Cock-a-doodle-doo !
What did I tell you ? "

" Oh, my ! · Oh, my ! " said Winky.
" I did not want to be bad.
I just wanted to play with it."

" You should listen to Speck,"
said Billy.
" Specky does not want you to play
with her baby chicks."

Winky said, " Specky does not like
me very much.
I will not play with her
baby chicks again."

much

Read and Find —

Who counted the chicks.

How many chicks were yellow.

How many chicks were white.

How many chicks were black.

Who did not see the other chick.

Who heard the black chick call.

Who had little Black Chick.

Who jumped at Winky.

Who wanted to play with the chick.

Who did not want to be bad.

Who did not listen to Speck.

How much Specky liked Winky.

Who was under the hen.

One Rainy Day

Pat, pat, pat,

pat, pat, patter.

Down came the rain.

"We can not go out," said Billy.

"Shall I read to you, Jane?"

"Yes, Billy," said Jane.

"Please read a story to me.

I like to hear you read."

pat   rain

Fido, the Dog

Just then the children heard,
"Bowwow, bowwow!"

"That is Fido!" Billy said to Jane.

"Bowwow!" they heard again.

Billy opened the door and looked out.
He did not see anyone.

Jane went to the door.
She looked out, too.
She did not see anyone.

anyone

"Come, Fido!" called Billy.
"Come here to me."

But Fido barked, "Bowwow!"

"What is it, Fido?" asked Billy.
"Do you see anyone?"

Fido looked up into the tree.
He said, "Bowwow, bowwow!"

Billy looked up into the tree, too.
Then he began to laugh.

"What is it, Billy?" asked Jane.
"Do you see anyone?"

Billy said, "Look up in the tree."

Guess what Jane saw then!

There sat Winky in the tree.

He had on his raincoat.

He had on his boots.

And he had Jane's umbrella.

"Winky, come down!" called Jane.

"What are you doing in that tree?"

"Fido barks at me," said Winky.

"He will not let me come down."

coat   boots   umbrella

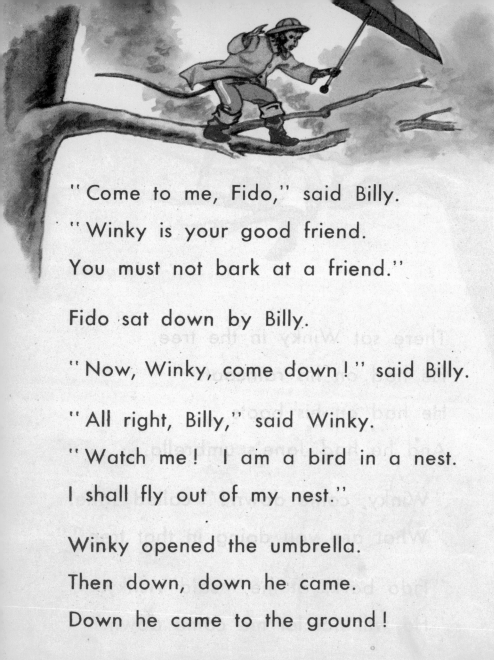

" Come to me, Fido," said Billy.

" Winky is your good friend.

You must not bark at a friend."

Fido sat down by Billy.

" Now, Winky, come down!" said Billy.

" All right, Billy," said Winky.

" Watch me! I am a bird in a nest.

I shall fly out of my nest."

Winky opened the umbrella.

Then down, down he came.

Down he came to the ground!

Billy asked,

"Where have you been?"

"Oh, I have been for a walk,"

said Winky.

"It rained and rained.

So I went for a walk.

I put on my raincoat and boots.

I took Jane's umbrella.

And I went for a walk.

Fido saw me.

He said, 'Bowwow, bowwow!'

So I ran up this tree."

been

Billy and Jane laughed.

"Fido did not know you," said Billy.
"He never saw a pet monkey
wear a raincoat and boots.
He never saw a monkey
with a girl's umbrella."

Jane said,
"Give the raincoat to me, Winky.
Give the boots to Billy.
Put the umbrella away.
Fido will know you then."

never   wear

Fido walked over to Winky.

He said, "Sniff, sniff, sniff, sniff."

Then he went to the raincoat.

He went to the boots.

He went to the umbrella.

"Sniff, sniff, sniff," he said.

Then he sat down by Winky.

His tail began to pat, pat, pat.

Do you know why?

sniff   why

What Am I?

1. I am not the umbrella.
   I am not the boots.
   You wear me when it rains.
   What am I? Draw me.

2. I never saw a pet monkey
   wear a raincoat and boots.
   I said, "Sniff, sniff, sniff."
   My tail went pat, pat, pat.
   What am I? Draw me.

3. I am not a raincoat.
   I had been for a walk.
   Fido barked at me.
   Do you know why?
   What am I? Draw me.

Cock-a-doodle-doo !

Words by
Myrtle B. Quinlan

Music by
Merle Montgomery

Gaily

Speck, the roost-er, said one day,

"Lis-ten now, hear what I say ! Cock-a-doo-dle-doo!

Play with Pol-ly and Bun-ny Lee, And play with Fi-do, too. But

Slower

do not play with the ba-by chicks, Or Speck-y won't like you, Or

Slower yet

Speck-y won't like you."

Farm Work

Bossy, the Cow

Grandfather came out of the house
with a milk pail.

"I am going to milk Bossy, the cow,"
he said to Billy and Jane.

"Do you want to go with me?"

"Yes, yes!" said the children.

"May I go, too?" asked Winky.

"Yes, you may go," said Grandfather.

pail

"Moo, moo," said Bossy, the cow.
"Where is my supper?"

"Here is your supper,"
said Grandfather.
"May we have some good milk?"

"Moo, moo," said Bossy.
"You may have some milk."

supper

Bossy ate her supper.

Grandfather sat down and milked
into the big pail.

"How much milk does Bossy give?"
asked Billy.

"We shall see," said Grandfather.
"This pail holds ten quarts of milk.
Four quarts make one gallon."

"Will Bossy give one gallon of milk?"
asked Winky.

"We shall see," said Grandfather.

holds   quarts   gallon

"How white the milk is!" said Jane.
"I like to drink fresh milk."

"You may have some milk,"
said Grandfather.
"But you will need a cup.
Ask Grandmother for some cups,"
he said to Billy.

"Yes, Grandfather," said Billy.
And he ran to the house for the cups.

drink   cup

"Hold out your cup, Jane,"
said Grandfather.
"And I will fill it with milk."

"Thank you, Grandfather," said Jane.

Then Grandfather filled Billy's cup
with milk.

"Thank you, Grandfather," said Billy.

fill

"I should like some fresh milk, too,"
said Winky to Billy.

"Oh, Winky!" said Billy.
"I did not get a cup for you.
Here! You may have my cup."

"No, no!" said Grandfather.
"Winky does not need a cup.
He can drink without a cup."

"Without a cup!" said Billy.

"Without a cup!" said Jane.

"How?" asked Winky.

"You will see," said Grandfather.
"You will see."

"Open your mouth," said Grandfather.

Guess what Grandfather did then!
He milked right into Winky's mouth.
He filled Winky's mouth with milk.

"What fun!" laughed Billy and Jane.

"Thank you, Grandfather," said Winky.
"I like to drink milk without a cup.
I have had a good supper."

mouth

Can You Tell —

Who milked Bossy, the cow?

Who milked into the big pail?

Who wanted to drink fresh milk?

Who ran to get some cups?

Who asked Grandmother for cups?

Who asked Jane to hold out the cup?

Who filled Billy's cup with milk?

Who opened his mouth?

Who filled Winky's mouth with milk?

Who liked to drink without a cup?

How many quarts make one gallon?

How much milk you drink?

Baby Calf

" Moo, moo, moo ! " said Bossy, the cow.

" Quick ! " said Grandfather.
" Climb on the fence !
Here comes Bossy's baby calf.
Do not get close to her baby calf."

" Moo, moo," said Bossy to her calf.
" Come to your mother."

calf   fence

Billy and Jane sat on the fence.
Winky sat on the fence, too.
They watched the baby calf
get his supper.

"What is the calf's name?" asked Jane.

"Wobbles," said Grandfather.

"Wobbles?" said Billy.

"Why did you name him Wobbles?"
asked Jane.

name   Wobbles

"Watch him," said Grandfather.
"Watch him as he walks.
See him wobble this way and that."

"Oh, I know now!" laughed Jane.
"That is why you named him Wobbles.
He wobbles this way and that way."

"See him get his bath!" said Billy.

"Yes," said Grandfather.
"When Wobbles gets his supper,
Bossy gives him a bath."

way   bath

Just then Billy dropped his cup.

It dropped close to Bossy.

"I will get your cup," said Winky.

Winky jumped off the high fence.

He ran to get Billy's cup.

dropped   ·   off

Bossy did not see the cup.

But she saw Winky.

And she ran at him!

"Run, Winky, run!" called Billy.

"Jump, Winky, jump!" called Jane.

And Winky did jump!
He jumped right over the fence!

Winky Is a Hero

Billy jumped off the fence.

He ran to Winky and asked,

"Are you hurt, Winky? Are you hurt?"

"Oh, no, no!" said Winky.

"I am not hurt.

But Bossy does not like me."

"Bossy likes you, Winky," said Billy.

"She just does not want you

too close to her baby calf.

But you are a brave monkey.

You are a hero."

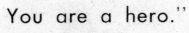

hero   brave

Winky looked at Billy.

"What is a hero?" he asked.

"A hero does something brave,"
said Billy.
"You did something brave.
So you are a hero."

Jane sang, "Winky is a hero!

Winky is a hero!"

Winky laughed. He was happy.
He was very, very happy.
Do you know why?

Tell the Right Words

1. Billy and Jane sat on —
   the house, the fence, the car.

2. Bossy's calf was named —
   Fido, Bunny Lee, Wobbles.

3. Billy dropped —
   his cup, his raincoat, his boots.

4. Winky jumped off —
   the fence, the table, the airport.

5. Winky did something —
   bad, brave, small.

6. Winky was —
   a baby calf, a parrot, a hero.

7. Bossy gave Wobbles —
   a pail, a bath, a name.

Two Gallons of Milk

"Look at the bottles!"
said Billy to Grandfather.
"How much milk did Bossy give?"

"Let us find out," said Grandfather.
"Why not count the bottles?"

Billy counted eight bottles of milk.

"Four quarts make one gallon,"
said Winky.

"And eight quarts make two gallons,"
said Billy.
"So Bossy gave two gallons of milk."

bottles   eight   gave

Grandmother came to the door.

Jane said,
"Guess how much milk Bossy gave!"

"Four quarts!" said Grandmother.

"Not four quarts," said Jane.

"Six quarts!" said Grandmother.

"Not six quarts," said Jane.

"Eight quarts!" said Grandmother.

"Yes, she gave eight quarts," said Jane.

"Four quarts make one gallon,"
said Winky.

"Eight quarts make two gallons."

"I shall deliver the milk early
in the morning," said Grandfather.
"Do you want to go with me?"

"Yes, yes," said Billy and Jane.

"May I deliver milk, too?" asked Winky.

"Yes, you may deliver milk, too,"
laughed Grandfather.

"Oh, what fun, what fun!"
said Winky.
"It will be fun to deliver milk
early in the morning."

deliver   early

Something to Tell

1. I am a boy.

   I counted eight quarts of milk.

   Tell something I said.

2. I am Bossy, the cow.

   I gave two gallons of milk.

   Tell something I said.

3. I am Grandfather.

   I deliver milk early in the morning.

   Tell something I said.

4. I am Winky, the monkey.

   I wanted to deliver the milk.

   Tell something I said.

Time to Get Up

" Cock-a-doodle-doo ! "
said Speck, the rooster.
" Cock-a-doodle-doo !   Listen to me.
It is time to get up ! "

Winky sat up in his bed.
He looked out the window.
" This is early," he said.
" Grandfather said to get up early."

bed

Billy sat up in bed.
He looked at the clock.

"Tick, tock, four o'clock!"
said the tick-tock clock.

"Oh, my!" said Billy. "Four o'clock!
We must hurry and get dressed.
We are going with Grandfather
to deliver milk.
We must call Jane, too."

Early Breakfast

" Good morning, Grandmother,"
said Jane.
" Here we are all dressed
and ready for breakfast."

" Oh, good morning, children ! "
said Grandmother.

" Where is Grandfather ? " asked Billy.

" Grandfather ate breakfast early,"
said Grandmother.
" He went to milk the cows.
Eat your breakfast now."

Work to Do

"Here you are!" said Grandfather.
"You are up very early."

"Winky waked me," said Jane.

"Speck, the rooster, waked me,"
said Winky.

"Grandfather waked the rooster,"
laughed Grandmother.

"All right," said Grandfather.
"Let's go now.   We have work to do."

"Good-by, Grandmother," Jane said.
"Thank you for a good breakfast."

Did ?

Did the rooster wake Winky ?

Did anyone wake the rooster ?

Did Jane get dressed early ?

Did Winky sit up in bed ?

Did Jane thank Grandmother ?

Who ?

Who had been to milk the cows ?

Who looked at the clock ?

Who ate breakfast early ?

Who had work to do ?

Why ?

Why did Grandfather get up early ?

Why did the children get up early ?

Something to Tell

Why did Billy go to the airport?

Who went up in the airplane?

Why was Winky in the box?

What stopped on the ground?

Who hopped behind Bunny Lee?

Who had the little black chick?

Who was under Mother Hen?

Who was wearing a raincoat?

Why did Fido bark at Winky?

Who ate her supper?

Who gave Wobbles a bath?

Who dropped his cup?

Who counted eight quarts of milk?

Who did something brave?

Delivering Milk

"How much milk do we have?"
Billy asked Grandfather.

"You may count the bottles,"
said Grandfather.

So Billy began to count.
He counted twenty-four quarts of milk.

"Oh, my!" said Winky.

"Twenty-four quarts of milk!"

twenty

Grandfather drove the car.

Billy and Winky sang,

"Down the road, down the road,

Down the road we go,

Delivering milk, delivering milk,

Delivering milk, just so!"

drove   road

Grandfather drove down the road.
When he came to a railroad track,
he stopped the car.
He looked up the railroad track.
He looked down the railroad track.
Then he drove across the track.

railroad   track

"Always look for trains,"
said Grandfather.
"Never go across the track
when a train is close."

"You watch for trains here," said Jane.
"We watch for cars at home.
We always look up the street.
We look down the street.
Then we hurry across the street."

Billy said,
"Birds do not need to look for trains.
They can fly across the tracks."

"That is right," said Grandfather.
"Birds do fly across railroad tracks.
But we are not birds."

always   trains

Grandfather stopped the car
at a small white house.

He left two quarts of milk
at the door of the house.

The children watched him.

When he came to the car,
he had two empty bottles.

"I left two quarts of milk
at this house yesterday," he said.
"Here are the empty bottles."

left   empty   yesterday

Grandfather stopped the car again.

"Let me deliver the milk this time,"
said Billy.

Billy took a bottle filled with milk.
He left it at the door of the house.
When he came to the car,
he had an empty bottle.

"This bottle was filled with milk
yesterday," he said to Grandfather.
"But it is empty now."

"Grandfather filled my mouth with milk
yesterday," said Winky.
"But it is empty now."

Grandfather laughed at Winky.

an

Grandfather stopped the car
many times.
The children delivered the milk.

"I can deliver milk, too," said Winky.

"All right," said Grandfather.
"There is just one bottle left.
You may leave it at that white house."

Winky took the bottle of milk.
He looked up and down the street.
Then he ran across the street
to the pretty white house.

leave

A woman came to the door.

"Good morning," said Winky.
"Here is your milk."

The woman looked at Winky.
"What a surprise!" she said.
"I never saw a monkey deliver milk."

"Oh, I am a pet monkey!" said Winky.
"I like to deliver milk."

The woman laughed.
She gave Winky an empty bottle.

"Thank you," said Winky.
Then he ran to Grandfather's car.

woman

Find and Read —

"You may count the bottles."

"Twenty-four quarts of milk!"

Grandfather drove down the road.

He looked up the railroad track.

"Always look for trains."

"You watch for trains here."

"We always look up the street."

"I left two quarts of milk yesterday."

"Here are the empty bottles."

"You may leave it at that white house."

A woman came to the door.

"I never saw a monkey deliver milk."

The woman laughed.

She gave Winky an empty bottle.

Come, Get Your Milk!

Words by
Myrtle B. Quinlan

Music by
Merle Montgomery

Moderately Fast

Oh, here I come with
So, fill your cups with

good fresh milk For you to drink to - day.   I'll
good fresh milk. Drink it and you will see   That

leave some here, I'll leave some there, Then I shall go my
you will grow up big and tall. Come, get your milk from

way.
me!

103

Farm Fun

Nicky, the Horse

One morning the children saw Nicky,
who was eating grass.

"Come, Nicky!" called Grandfather.
"Here is an apple for you."

"Most horses like apples,"
said Billy.

"Most monkeys like apples, too,"
said Winky.

Grandfather laughed.
"I know you like apples," he said.
"Here is an apple for you.
And here are two for Jane and Billy."

apple   most

Riding Nicky

Grandfather patted the horse's nose.
"Nicky," he said, "see Jane and Billy.
They want a ride."

"Winky wants a ride, too," said Billy.

Grandfather put Jane on Nicky's back.
"Good old Nicky!" said Grandfather.
"You must not run with Jane."

Jane patted Nicky.
"Good old Nicky!" she said.
"I like to ride on your back."

back

"Now Billy may have a ride,"
said Jane.

"I can get on Nicky's back,"
said Billy. "I want to go fast."

"Hold on!" said Grandfather.
"Do not go too fast."

"Oh, I will hold on all right!"
said Billy. "But I want to go fast."

fast

"Let Winky have a ride now,"
said Grandfather.

Winky jumped up on Nicky's back.
"I want to go very fast," he said.

"Hold on, Winky!" said Billy.

"Oh, I will hold on," said Winky.
"But I want to go very fast."

Nicky looked at Winky.

"Run fast, Nicky!" said Winky.

And Nicky did run fast — very fast!

"Hold on, Winky!" the children cried.

Nicky looked around at Winky.
"I shall have some fun," he said.

around

Nicky looked around at Winky again.

Can you guess what he did?

He ran very fast.

He ran under the apple tree.

"Jump, Winky, jump!" cried Billy.

And Winky jumped!

He jumped off Nicky's back.

He jumped into the big apple tree.

Then he laughed at Nicky.

"This is fun!" he said.

Yes — No

Nicky took an apple in his mouth.

Most horses like apples.

Most monkeys eat grass.

Winky patted Nicky's back.

Jane wanted to wear a coat.

Nicky ran fast with Billy.

Nicky looked around at Winky.

Winky jumped behind the tree.

Nicky gave Winky a ride.

Jane wanted to hold a picture.

An apple dropped on Billy's nose.

Billy drove the car yesterday.

Nicky had been to school.

Fluffy, the Cat

"Billy!" called Grandmother.

"Have you seen Fluffy today?"

"No, Grandmother," said Billy.

"I have not seen her."

"We will look for her, Grandmother,"
said Jane.

"Yes," said Winky.

"Let's go look for Fluffy now."

Fluffy   seen

Billy saw Specky, the hen,
with her ten baby chicks.

"Good morning, Mother Specky,"
said Billy.
"Have you seen Fluffy, the cat?"

"Cluck, cluck, cluck," said Specky.
"I have not seen Fluffy.
Ask Speck, the rooster.
Perhaps he has seen her."

perhaps

They saw Speck, the rooster,
who was on a high fence.

"Good morning, Speck," said Billy.
"Fluffy, the cat, is lost.
Have you seen her?"

"Cock-a-doodle-doo," said Speck.
"No, Billy, I have not seen her.
Ask Bossy, the cow.
Perhaps she has seen her."

lost

The children saw Bossy, the cow.

"Bossy," said Jane, "Fluffy is lost.
Have you seen her?"

"Moo, moo," said Bossy.
"I have not seen her."

Just then the children saw Wobbles,
the baby calf.

"Moo, moo!" said Bossy to her calf.
"Come to your mother."

"Quick!" cried Winky.
"Climb on the fence!
Bossy does not want us close
to her baby calf."

The children jumped off the fence.
They walked on and on.
They saw Nicky, the horse.

"Nicky," said Billy,
"Fluffy, the cat, is lost.
Have you seen her?"

"Yes, I have," said Nicky.
"And I was not glad to see her."

"Not glad to see her!" said Jane.

"Why?" asked Billy.

"Look in the barn," said Nicky.
"Look in the barn and you will see."

The children ran into the barn.

barn

Jane called, "Fluffy, Fluffy!
Where are you? Where are you?"

"Mew, mew, mew," they heard.

"What is that?" asked Jane.
"I heard something."

"Mew, mew, mew, mew,"
the children heard again.

Billy looked around.
"That must be Fluffy," he said.
"But where can she be?"

The children began to look.
They ran this way and that.
They looked here. They looked there.
Winky looked and looked, too.

Just then they heard,
" Mew, mew, mew, mew."

Billy looked down.
He looked down in Nicky's hay.
Perhaps you can guess what he saw !

hay

"Oh, look, Jane, look!" cried Billy.

"Fluffy is not lost.

Here she is in Nicky's hay.

And here are some baby kittens!"

"Baby kittens!" said Jane.

"Little baby kittens!" said Winky.

"Let's count them," said Billy.

So Billy counted one, two,
three, four, five.

"Five little baby kittens!" he said.

kittens   five

" Come on ! " said Jane.

" Let's tell Grandmother.

She will be glad we found Fluffy."

" I know now why Nicky
was not happy," said Winky.

" Yes," laughed Billy.

" He did not want Fluffy in his hay."

" Perhaps he did not like the kittens
in his hay," said Jane.

The children ran out of the barn.

They ran to the house.

They cried, "Fluffy is not lost!
Fluffy is not lost!"

"She is in the barn," said Billy.

"She is in Nicky's hay," said Jane.

"She has five baby kittens," said Winky.

"Oh, she has!" laughed Grandmother.
"I must see them, too."

A Bed for Fluffy

"This basket will make a fine bed
for Fluffy and her baby kittens,"
said Grandmother.

Billy put Fluffy in the basket.
Jane put the kittens in the basket.

"Let me touch one, Jane," said Winky.
"Please let me touch one."

Fluffy said, "Mew, mew, mew."
Then she began
to give her babies a bath.
Do you know how?

basket

Tell the Right One

1. Polly, the parrot, was lost.
   Fluffy, the cat, was lost.

2. Billy found Fluffy in Nicky's hay.
   Jane found a kitten in the house.

3. Three rabbits were in the barn.
   Five kittens were in the hay.

4. Fluffy's bed was in the basket.
   Jane's bed was in the basket.

5. Bossy, the cow, had seen Fluffy.
   Nicky, the horse, had seen Fluffy.

6. Winky touched the kittens.
   Specky touched the kittens.

Country Fair

One day Grandfather asked,
"Do you want to go to the fair?"

"To a fair!" said Billy.
"Oh, that will be fun!"

"Do you have fairs in the country?"
asked Jane.

"Yes, Jane," said Grandfather.
"We have country fairs here.
You have city fairs at home."

country   fair   city

"Will the country fair be like
our city fair?" asked Billy.

"Our country fair is not just like
your city fair," said Grandfather.

"What shall we see at the fair?"
asked Jane.

"You will see many people,"
said Grandfather.
"You will see many animals.
People take their best animals
to the country fair."
Grandfather laughed.
"You know, people like to show off
their best animals," he said.

people   their   show

"Do people take just animals
to the fair?" asked Billy.

"No, Billy," said Grandfather.
"They take their best fruit
and vegetables, too.
People like to show off their
best fruit and vegetables."

"I like to eat fruit and vegetables,"
said Winky.

Grandfather laughed at Winky.
"You are a funny monkey!" he said.

vegetables

"Let's take our best animal
to this country fair," said Billy.

"What animal do you want to take?"
asked Grandfather.

"We could take Wobbles, the calf,"
said Jane.

"Oh, no, no!" said Winky.
"Bossy would not like that.
You know she is a funny cow.
I don't think we should take Wobbles."

could   would

"We could take Fluffy, the cat,"
said Billy.

"No, no!" said Jane.
"Fluffy must not leave her kittens."

"Oh, that is right," said Billy.

"We could take Bunny Lee
and her little rabbits three,"
said Winky.

"Yes, yes!" said Billy and Jane.
"Bunny Lee would like to go
to the country fair."

"Fine!" said Grandfather.
"You may take Bunny Lee
and her little rabbits three."

Tell the Right Words

1. The fair was in —
   the city, the country, the train.

2. People like to show off their —
   best animals, best oatmeal.

3. Fruit and vegetables are good —
   to wear, to eat, to color.

4. Bunny Lee would like to go —
   to the fair, to the city.

5. The children could take —
   Wobbles, Fluffy, Bunny Lee.

At the Fair

Billy and Jane were up early
the next morning. They put Bunny Lee
and her babies into a big basket.
Then Grandfather took them all
to the country fair.

He stopped the car at the fair grounds.
The children took Bunny Lee's basket
across the road.
They saw many people.
They saw many animals.
They saw fruits and vegetables, too.

"Here is a cage for Bunny Lee
and her little rabbits three,"
said Grandfather.

"This is a fine cage," said Billy.
"Bunny Lee will be next
to some other rabbits.
She can see the other animals, too."

"Look at the baby rabbits," said Jane.
"They must be warm in that cage."

"They are warm," said Billy.
"I will get them some grass
and some cool water."

warm

A man put number "25"
on Bunny Lee's cage.

"Why did the man put number '25'
on Bunny Lee's cage?" asked Billy.

"Twenty-five is her number,"
said Grandfather.
"She may be the best rabbit here.
Then she will get a prize."

"A prize!" said Jane.
"Bunny Lee would like that."

"I should like a prize, too,"
laughed Winky.

man   prize

Grandfather and the children walked
around the fair grounds.
They went by a lemonade stand.
The man at the stand called,
"Right this way, right this way!
Pink lemonade, pink lemonade!
Drink pink lemonade!"

"I like pink lemonade," said Winky.

"This man has good lemonade,"
said Grandfather.
"Let's get some at his stand."

lemonade   stand

The Prize

"Right this way, right this way!"
called a man in a loud voice.
"See who gets a prize!"

"Hurry, Winky!" said Billy.
"Drink your lemonade.
We must go to Bunny Lee."

"Will she get a prize?" asked Winky.

"We shall know soon," said Billy.
"Hurry now! Drink your lemonade!"

loud   voice   soon

"Stand here," said Grandfather:
"We can see Bunny Lee's cage."

"We can see the man
with the loud voice, too," said Jane.
"Here he comes with many ribbons.
Some ribbons are red.
And some ribbons are blue."

ribbons

" What are the ribbons for ? "
asked Jane.

" A blue ribbon is First Prize, "
said Grandfather.

" A red ribbon is Second Prize. "

" The blue ribbon is the best of all, "
said Billy.

" Will Bunny Lee get a blue ribbon ? "
asked Winky.

" Perhaps, " said Grandfather.
" We shall know very soon. "

first   second

"First Prize, Second Prize!
First Prize, Second Prize!"
called the man with the loud voice.

He gave blue ribbons and red ribbons.
Then he came to Bunny Lee's cage.
Bunny Lee looked at the man.
Her funny little nose began
to wiggle, wiggle, wiggle.

The man laughed and said,
"First Prize to Bunny Lee
and her little rabbits three!"

"Oh, look at Bunny Lee!" said Jane.

"She is proud of her fine family."

"I am proud of Bunny Lee, too,"
said Grandfather. "But come now!
We must take her home.
Grandmother will be looking for us."

"It's fun to go to fairs with you,"
Jane said to Grandfather.

"Thank you," said Grandfather.
"It is fun for me, too."

proud   family

Something to Tell

1. Have you been to a fair?

   Did you see many people?

   Did you see many animals?

   Tell one other thing you saw.

2. Did you go to a stand?

   Did you drink pink lemonade?

   Did you eat fresh fruit?

   Tell one other thing you did.

3. Did a man give you a prize?

   Was it First Prize?

   Was it Second Prize?

   Was the blue ribbon First Prize?

   Was the red ribbon Second Prize?

Gobbler's Family

One morning Billy and Jane
were sitting on the barnyard fence.
Winky sat on the fence with them.
They were watching the turkey family.
Mother Turkey was proud of her family.
Father Turkey was proud, too.

"Look at Father Gobbler!" said Billy.
"See how proud he is!"

Gobbler   barnyard   turkey

"Father Gobbler is king," said Jane.
"He is king of this barnyard.
He is proud of his family."

"Watch him!" said Billy.
"Look at his big tail feathers!"

"Gobble, gobble, gobble!"
said Father Gobbler in a loud voice.
"Look at me! How proud I am!
See my tail feathers!
I am king of this barnyard.
I am proud of my turkey family."

king   feathers

Winky said,

"I want to be a king, too."

"You can not be a king," said Jane.
"You have no feathers for your tail."

"I shall ask Father Gobbler
for some feathers," said Winky.
"I shall tie them on my tail.
Then I shall be a king, too."

"Tie them on your tail!" said Billy.

"Yes, tie them on my tail," said Winky.
"Then I shall be a proud king."

Billy and Jane laughed and laughed.

tie

Just then the children saw Specky.
They saw her ten baby chicks, too.

"Specky is hungry," said Billy.
"Let's get something for her to eat."

"Grandmother will give us something,"
said Jane.

Winky and Gobbler

As Jane and Billy came
out of the house, they heard,
"Gobble, gobble, gobble!"

They ran to the hen house door.
There was Winky with Father Gobbler.

"Winky, Winky!" cried Jane.
"What are you doing?"

"I am getting some feathers
for my tail," said Winky.

"Let Father Gobbler go," said Billy.

"You are a naughty monkey.

You are a very naughty monkey."

Winky let Father Gobbler go.

The turkey said, "Gobble, gobble!"

Jane and Billy looked at Winky.

But Winky did not look at them.

He looked down at the feathers.

"They are not yours," said Jane.

"They belong to Father Gobbler.

You should never take things

that do not belong to you."

naughty   belong

Billy asked,
"Why did you do it, Winky?"

"I wanted to be a king," said Winky.
"I wanted some feathers
for my tail."

"Why didn't you ask Father Gobbler
for some feathers?" said Billy.

"I did ask him," said Winky.

"What did he say?" asked Jane.

"What did he say?" said Winky.
"He said, 'Gobble, gobble.
Monkeys do not have tail feathers.'"

say

"What did you do then?" asked Billy.

"I caught Father Gobbler,"
said Winky.
"I caught him by the tail.
I pulled and I pulled.
I pulled out three tail feathers."

"You are a naughty monkey, Winky,"
said Billy. "Come, Jane.
We will not play with him."

caught   pulled

Winky was sad.

He was very, very sad.

He looked at the turkey feathers.

He said, "They do not belong to me.

I can not tie them on my tail.

I do not want to be naughty.

I want to be good.

What shall I do?

Oh, what shall I do?"

Again Billy and Jane heard
Father Gobbler's loud voice.
Again they ran to the hen house.

There was Winky with Father Gobbler.

"Winky, Winky!" cried Billy.
"What is wrong?
What are you doing now?"

"Oh my, oh my!" said Winky.
"The feathers do not belong to me.
I am trying to put them back."

wrong   trying

Right — Wrong

Jane sat on the barnyard fence.
Billy tied a ribbon on Winky.

Winky was king of the barnyard.
Father Gobbler had big tail feathers.

Winky caught Father Gobbler.
Wobbles was trying to be naughty.

The feathers belonged to the turkey.
Jane could see nothing at night.

Something was wrong with Specky.
Winky pulled out three feathers.

Winky tried to put the feathers back.
Billy caught the cup as it dropped.

Gobble, Gobble

Words by
Myrtle B. Quinlan

Music by
Zoo B. Barnett

Lively

"Oh, gob-ble, gob-ble, gob-ble!" Said Turk-ey to Wink-y one

day. "Oh, gob-ble, gob-ble, gob-ble! There is some-thing I want to

say. Don't get close to Wob-bles As he runs and plays a-

bout. And please don't catch me by my tail And

Slower   Faster

pull my feath-ers out!"

Story Time

Warm Summer Day

One warm summer day Billy said,
"Our visit at the farm
will soon be over."

"Yes," said Jane. "But we have
many days for play
before we go back to school."

summer   visit   before

Stories about School

"Perhaps you may make another visit before you go back to school," said Grandmother.

"Before we go back to school!" said Winky. "I like to go to school."

"Are you good at school, Winky?" asked Grandfather.

"I try to be good," said Winky.

"What do you do at school?" asked Grandmother. "Tell us about it."

"We read, and we write," said Billy. "We draw pictures and make things."

about

"Can you say 'Jack Be Nimble'?"
asked Grandmother.

"Jack be nimble,
Jack be quick,
Jack jump over
The candlestick," said Jane.

"We wrote a story about Jack,"
said Billy.

"And we wrote about Mary, too,"
said Jane. "Mary is my friend."

"We draw funny pictures at school,"
said Billy.

"I like to draw with crayons,"
said Winky.
"But one day I ate them."

"Ate them!" said Grandfather.

"Yes, I ate them," laughed Winky.
"One day I was very hungry.
So I ate my crayons."

"Ha, ha, ha!" laughed Grandfather.
"Oh, you funny monkey!" he said.

"We made cocoa at school, too,"
said Jane.

"How?" asked Grandmother.

Jane sang,
  "Put in the sugar, so!
  Put in the cocoa, ho!
  Put in the water,
  Put in the milk,
  And stir, my, oh!"

"Stir what?" asked Grandfather.

"Stir sugar, cocoa, water, and milk,"
said Jane.

"Good!" said Grandfather.
"You shall make cocoa for me."

"I try to be good at school,"
said Winky.
"But one day I was greedy."

"Tell us about it," said Grandmother.

"We made some cocoa," said Winky.
"It was too hot to drink.
I did not want to let it cool.
I wanted to drink it. It burned me."

"You will not be greedy again,"
said Jane.

"No," said Winky.
"I will never be greedy again."

School Games

"We play many games at school,"
said Billy.

"What games do you play?"
asked Grandmother.

"We play ' May I ?' games
and number games," said Billy.

"I know one more game," said Jane.

"What is it?" asked Billy.

"It is the word game,"
said Jane.

"Oh, yes!" said Billy.
"That is a good game, too."

"Let us play the word game,"
said Grandfather.

"All right," said Billy.
"Can you think of two words
that sound like 'book'?"

Grandfather said, "The words
'took' and 'look' sound like 'book.'"

"Good for you, Grandfather!"
laughed Billy.
"Took, look, and book!
Now you think of some words
that sound alike."

book

Grandfather said, "I am thinking
of two words that sound like 'hay.'"

"Are you thinking of the words
'play' and 'day'?" asked Jane.

"No, Jane," said Grandfather.
"I am not thinking of the words
'play' and 'day.'"

"Are you thinking of the words
'say' and 'way'?" asked Billy.

"Yes, I am thinking of the words
'say' and 'way,'" said Grandfather.

"Play, day, hay, way, and say!
They do sound alike," said Jane.

"And they look alike, too,"
said Grandmother.

"Do you think of a game, Winky?"
asked Billy.

"The fresh-air game," said Winky.
"I like it best of all."

Then Winky sang,
  "Jane and Billy, do you know
  Good fresh air will make you grow?"

Billy and Jane sang,
  "Winky, Winky, we do know
  Good fresh air will make us grow."

Work and Play

"The boys and I went to Lee's Store,"
said Winky.
"Mr. Lee gave us two boxes.
The big box was for my table.
The little box was for my chair."
Winky looked at Jane.
"The girls made a pretty pillow
for my chair," he said.

"Then the girls sat on the pillow,"
said Billy.

Jane laughed. "Miss Ward sat
on the pillow, too," she said.

"Oh, I know something funny,"
said Winky.

"What is it?" asked Grandfather.

"The boys were making my table.
I wanted to work and hammer, too.
I missed the nail and hit my tail."

"Did it hurt?" asked Grandmother.

"Yes, it hurt then," said Winky.
"But it is funny now."

"Ho, ho, ho!" laughed Grandfather.
"Winky missed the nail
and hit his tail!"

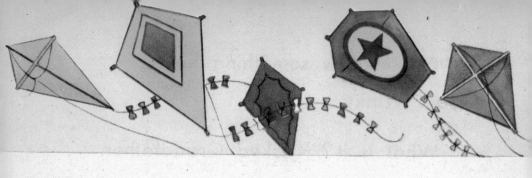

"We made kites in the spring,"
said Billy.
"One day I pulled my kite down
into a tree. I pulled and pulled.
But it was caught.
It would not come out."

"Then Winky was a brave monkey,"
said Jane. "He climbed the tree
and found Billy's kite."

"I like to do things for Billy,"
said Winky.

spring

Tell

Tell one thing about Billy's sister.

Tell one thing about Jane's brother.

Tell one thing about warm summer.

Tell one thing about spring.

Find

Find who is six years old.

Find the words "visit" and "before."

Find the words "book" and "look."

Find the words "try" and "cry."

Show

Show a picture of Grandmother.

Show a picture of Grandfather.

Show a picture in your book.

Show a picture of a farm pet.

Grandmother's Story

"Grandmother," said Billy,
"please tell us a story."

"A story, a story!" said Grandmother.
"What story shall I tell?
Let me think."

Winky said, "Let Grandmother think."

"I know!" said Grandfather.
"Tell about the baby duck who
liked to swim."

"Oh, yes!" said Grandmother.
"I shall tell about Blinky, the duck."

duck   swim   Blinky

Blinky, the Duck

Blinky was a little baby duck
who liked to swim.

One warm summer day he said
to his mother, "I am three weeks old.
May I go for a swim?"

"Quack, quack," said Mother Duck.
"You are just a baby.
Take your nap now.
Then I shall take you for a swim."

Mother Duck closed her eyes.
Soon she was fast asleep.

weeks   quack   nap

The sun was warm.
And it was very still.
Blinky closed his eyes.
He could see the cool water.
He opened his eyes and blinked
at the big warm sun.

"I am not a baby," he said.
"I am three weeks old.
I do not want a nap.
I want to swim in the cool water."

Guess what Blinky did then!

He walked to the barnyard.
He could not walk very fast.
His feet were too big.

Blinky looked down at his feet.
"You are no good for walking,"
he said.
"But you are very good for swimming.
And I do like to swim."

feet

Blinky walked into the barnyard.
It was very still.

"What are you doing here?"
asked Specky, the hen.
"Look at your funny feet.
They are not good for walking."

"But they are good for swimming,"
said Blinky. "And I want to swim.
May your chicks go with me?"

"Cluck, cluck, cluck!" said Specky.
"No, indeed!
My chicks are taking a nap.
You should be taking a nap, too."

indeed

Blinky walked on.

He saw Speck, the rooster.

"Quack, quack," he said to Speck.

"I am not a baby duck.

I am three weeks old.

I do not want to take a nap.

I want to go for a swim.

Will you go with me?"

"Swim, indeed!" said Speck.

"Roosters do not swim.

I am going to sleep.

You should be taking a nap, too."

Blinky was very tired.

But still he walked on and on.

He asked every animal he saw

to go for a swim.

But every animal wanted

to take a nap.

Blinky sat down by the road.

He looked at his feet and said,

"You are good for swimming,

but no good for walking."

He looked all about him.

"I am so tired!" he said.

"What shall I do?

Oh, what shall I do?"

tired   every

Just then Blinky heard something.

He looked up.

He saw Nicky, the horse.

"What is wrong?" asked Nicky.

"What are you doing here?"

"Oh, Nicky!" cried Blinky.

"I am a naughty duck.

I did not want to take a nap.

I wanted to go for a swim.

So I ran away. I am so tired!

What shall I do?"

Nicky looked at Blinky's feet.

"Get on my back," he said.

"I will take you home."

Blinky sat close to Mother Duck.

"Mother always knows best," he said.

"I am so tired!

I think I shall take a nap."

Blinky closed one eye.

Next he closed both eyes.

Soon he was asleep.

Yes, indeed!

Soon he was fast asleep!

Do You Know —

Who wanted to swim in cool water?

Who said, "Quack, quack"?

Who was three weeks old?

Who sat still in the sun?

Who wanted to take a nap?

Who asked every animal to swim?

Who looked at his feet?

Who said, "Swim, indeed"?

Who did something wrong?

Who was very tired?

Who took Blinky home?

Who sat close to Mother Duck?

Who closed both eyes?

Who went to sleep?

Early Autumn Days

One day Grandmother said,
"Autumn will soon be here."

"Yes," said Grandfather.
"And when the autumn days are over,
cold winter days will come.
Then most of the birds will go away.
And many of the animals
will sleep all winter."

autumn   cold   winter

"Do some animals sleep
all winter?" asked Jane.

"Yes," said Grandfather.

"Why do the birds go away?"
asked Billy.

"I know a very old story,"
said Grandfather.
"It tells about birds going away
and animals sleeping all winter.
Should you like to hear it?"

"Yes, yes!" said Billy and Jane.

Grandfather's Story

Autumn

One cool day in early autumn
some birds were visiting
with Mr. Turtle and Hop-Hop, the frog.

One of the little birds said,
"The warm summer is gone.
Cool autumn days like this
will soon be gone, too.
When the cold winter days come,
we shall go away."

"Go away!" said Hop-Hop, the frog.
"Where are you going?"

"Go away!" said Mr. Turtle.
"Why are you going?"

Turtle   frog   gone

"Most of us fly away in winter,"
said one of the birds.
"We go South where it is warm.
There is food in the South."

"But there is food here," said
the little frog.

"There is food here now," said a bird.
"But when it is cold and snow is
on the ground, we can not find it."

"When shall you be back?"
asked big Mr. Turtle.

"In the spring," said the bird.
"Look for us next spring
when the snow is gone."

South   food   snow

The days grew cooler and cooler.
Then one day the birds did not come
to the woods.

"They have gone," said Hop-Hop sadly.

"Yes," said big Mr. Turtle.
"They have gone South
where it is warm.
But they will be back next spring."

"How shall we know when it is spring?"
asked little Hop-Hop.

"We must not sleep this winter,"
said Mr. Turtle.
"Let's come to the woods every day.
We must be here when the birds
come back in the spring."

grew   woods

Winter

The days grew colder and colder.

Snow was on the ground.

Many animals did go to sleep.

And the woods were very still.

But every day Mr. Turtle and Hop-Hop,

the frog, came to look for the birds.

Then one day big Mr. Turtle
and Hop-Hop, the frog, grew sleepy.
They grew very sleepy, indeed.

"I am so tired and sleepy,"
said little Hop-Hop, the frog.
"Let's take one very small nap."

"All right," said big Mr. Turtle.
"Let's take one small nap!
Just one very small nap!"

Days and days and weeks and weeks
went by.
And do you know?
Big Mr. Turtle and little Hop-Hop
slept and slept and slept.

The woods were white with snow.
And still the two friends slept.

slept

Spring

Mr. Turtle and Hop-Hop, the frog,
slept and slept and slept.
Then one day their sleep was over.
They came out of the water
to look for their friends, the birds.
And what a surprise they had!

The snow was gone.
The woods were green.
And the sun was warm.

Hop-Hop looked at his friend,
Mr. Turtle, with eyes big and round.
"Why, spring is here!" he said.
"We have slept all winter!"

"That is right," laughed Mr. Turtle.
"Some animals do not need food
in winter. So they sleep.
But the birds need food.
So they fly away to the South."

Just then they heard,
"Hello, hello, down there!"

Hop-Hop and Mr. Turtle looked up.
There were their friends, the birds!
They had left the warm, sunny South
and come back to their home
in the woods.

Going Home

"Oh, thank you, Grandfather!"
said Jane.
"That was a very good story."

"Summer will soon be gone
for us, too," said Billy.
"And before we know it,
our visit will be over."

"Yes," said Grandmother.
"And we are going to miss you."

"Shall you miss me?" asked Winky.

"Yes, indeed!" said Grandfather.
"But perhaps you can visit us again
next summer."

Hop-Hop

Words by
Myrtle B. Quinlan

Music by
Zoo B. Barnett

1. Small Hop–Hop and the tur–tle Came to the woods one day To see their friends, the pret–ty birds, But the birds had gone a–way.
2. Soon Hop–Hop grew so sleep–y He could not stay a–wake. His good friend, Mis–ter Tur–tle, said, "Just one small nap we'll take!"
3. But Hop–Hop and the tur–tle He Slept weeks and weeks, and then, When they a–wak–ened from their sleep, The birds had come a–gain.

1st and 2nd endings

3rd ending

Slow down

Word List of " To and Fro "

This first reader, *To and Fro*, has 192 new words. It includes also the 76 used in the pre-primer, *Winky*, and the 158 used in the primer, *Day by Day*. This makes a total of only 426 different words, yet there are more than 10,000 running words. Every word conforms in placement and gradation to the accepted standards of Gates, Thorndike, Horn-Packer, and Buckingham-Dolch vocabulary studies.

Each new word is listed in the color-band of the page on which it is introduced and is again repeated one or more times within the next two pages. Of the 192 new words, 129 are repeated on the page where they first appear; 44 on the next page following; and 19 on the second page following.

Every new word has been used six times or more. The ratio of running words to new words is 53.4; the ratio of running words to different words is 24.0. The maximum number of new words per page is 3; the average number, 1.03.

1. car	11. just heard	23. ———	36. Bunny has
2. hurry airport airplane	12. ———	24. ground stopped	37. hop
3. hello	13. ———	25. glad	38. nothing nose wiggle
4. fun grand- mother grand- father	14. ———	26. ———	
	15. ———	27. ———	39. rabbit grass
	16. ride	28. ———	
	17. animals	29. ———	
5. ———	18. Bossy give Nicky	30. next pretty	40. door white
6. whirr went	19. Fido bark	31. her cage	41. black night
7. small houses	20. Polly parrot began	32. ———	42. ———
		33. as him	43. behind spotted
8. out	21. ———	34. swing	44. ———
9. ———	22. ———	35. ———	45. ———
10. ———			

46. Specky
    hen
    chicks
47. rooster
    cock-a-
    doodle-doo
    listen
48. ten
    cluck
    under
49. yellow
    four
50. other
51. ——
52. counted
53. ——
54. had
55. ——
56. much
57. ——
58. pat
    rain
59. anyone
60. ——
61. coat
    boots
    umbrella

62. ——
63. been
64. never
    wear
65. sniff
    why
66. ——
67. ——
68. pail
69. supper
70. holds
    quarts
    gallon
71. drink
    cup
72. fill
73. ——
74. mouth
75. ——
76. calf
    fence
77. name
    Wobbles
78. way
    bath
79. dropped
    off

80. ——
81. hero
    brave
82. ——
83. ——
84. bottles
    eight
    gave
85. ——
86. deliver
    early
87. ——
88. bed
89. ——
90. ——
91. ——
92. ——
93. ——
94. twenty
95. drove
    road
96. railroad
    track
97. always
    trains

98. left
    empty
    yesterday
99. an
100. leave
101. woman
102. ——
103. ——
104. apple
    most
105. back
106. fast
107. around
108. ——
109. ——
110. Fluffy
    seen
111. perhaps
112. lost
113. ——
114. barn
115. ——
116. hay
117. kittens
    five
118. ——

119. ——
120. basket
121. ——
122. country
     fair
     city
123. people
     their
     show
124. vege-
     tables
125. could
     would
126. ——
127. ——
128. ——
129. warm
130. man
     prize
131. lemon-
     ade
     stand
132. loud
     voice
     soon
133. ribbons

134. first
     second
135. ——
136. proud
     family
137. ——
138. Gobbler
     barnyard
     turkey
139. king
     feathers
140. tie
141. ——
142. ——
143. naughty
     belong
144. say
145. caught
     pulled
146. ——
147. wrong
     trying
148. ——
149. ——
150. summer
     visit
     before

151. about
152. ——
153. ——
154. ——
155. ——
156. ——
157. book
158. ——
159. ——
160. ——
161. ——
162. spring
163. ——
164. duck
     swim
     Blinky
165. weeks
     quack
     nap
166. sun
     still
167. feet
168. indeed
169. ——

170. tired
     every
171. ——
172. ——
173. ——
174. autumn
     cold
     winter
175. ——
176. Turtle
     frog
     gone
177. south
     food
     snow
178. grew
     woods
179. ——
180. ——
181. slept
182. ——
183. ——
184. ——
185. ——